Chloë Dick

If found, please phone

(502) 744-6787

Table of content

Movie	Page #

Table of content

Movie	Page #

Table of content

Movie	Page #

Bucket list for a year, 52 weeks. One movie a week

	Movie	Year of production
1	All twiglight movies	
2		
3		
4		
5		
6		
7		
8		
9		
10		
11		
12		
13		
14		
15		
16		
17		
18		
19		
20		

MOVIES

Bucket list

	Movie	Year of production
21		
22		
23		
24		
25		
26		
27		
28		
29		
30		
31		
32		
33		
34		
35		
36		
37		
38		
39		
40		

Bucket list

	Movie	Year of production
41		
42		
43		
44		
45		
46		
47		
48		
49		
50		
51		
52		

MOVIES

Title	| Date	|time
Rating (G,PG, G13, R)	|Genre/Style	

Storyline or plot	
My Favourite part was	
Memorable Quotes	
My critic thoughts	

Director		-----/5
Cast		-----/5
Screenplay		-----/5
Cinematography		-----/5
Special effects/animation		-----/5
Music		-----/5
Customs		-----/5
Overall Score		-----/5

Will I watch it again?

I would recommend it to

Notes & Memories e.g. the tickets

Title	| Date	|time
Rating (G,PG, G13, R)	|Genre/Style	

Storyline or plot	
My Favourite part was	
Memorable Quotes	
My critic thoughts	

Director	-----/5
Cast	-----/5
Screenplay	-----/5
Cinematography	-----/5
Special effects/animation	-----/5
Music	-----/5
Customs	-----/5
Overall Score	-----/5

Will I watch it again?

I would recommend it to

Notes & Memories e.g. the tickets

MOVIES

Title	Date	time
Rating (G,PG, G13, R)	Genre/Style	

Storyline or plot	
My Favourite part was	
Memorable Quotes	
My critic thoughts	

Director	-----/5
Cast	-----/5
Screenplay	-----/5
Cinematography	-----/5
Special effects/animation	-----/5
Music	-----/5
Customs	-----/5
Overall Score	-----/5

Will I watch it again?

I would recommend it to

Notes & Memories e.g. the tickets

MOVIES

Title	Date	time
Rating (G,PG, G13, R)	Genre/Style	

Storyline or plot	
My Favourite part was	
Memorable Quotes	
My critic thoughts	

Director		-----/5
Cast		-----/5
Screenplay		-----/5
Cinematography		-----/5
Special effects/animation		-----/5
Music		-----/5
Customs		-----/5
Overall Score		-----/5

Will I watch it again?

I would recommend it to

Notes & Memories e.g. the tickets

MOVIES

Title	| Date	|time
Rating (G,PG, G13, R)	|Genre/Style	

Storyline or plot	
My Favourite part was	
Memorable Quotes	
My critic thoughts	

Director		-----/5
Cast		-----/5
Screenplay		-----/5
Cinematography		-----/5
Special effects/animation		-----/5
Music		-----/5
Customs		-----/5
Overall Score		-----/5

Will I watch it again?

I would recommend it to

Notes & Memories e.g. the tickets

MOVIES

Title	Date	time
Rating (G,PG, G13, R)	Genre/Style	

Storyline or plot	
My Favourite part was	
Memorable Quotes	
My critic thoughts	

Director		-----/5
Cast		-----/5
Screenplay		-----/5
Cinematography		-----/5
Special effects/animation		-----/5
Music		-----/5
Customs		-----/5
Overall Score		-----/5

Will I watch it again?

I would recommend it to

Notes & Memories e.g. the tickets

MOVIES

Title	Date	time
Rating (G,PG, G13, R)	Genre/Style	

Storyline or plot	
My Favourite part was	
Memorable Quotes	
My critic thoughts	

Director	-----/5
Cast	-----/5
Screenplay	-----/5
Cinematography	-----/5
Special effects/animation	-----/5
Music	-----/5
Customs	-----/5
Overall Score	-----/5

Will I watch it again?

I would recommend it to

Notes & Memories e.g. the tickets

MOVIES

Title	Date	time
Rating (G,PG, G13, R)	Genre/Style	

Storyline or plot	
My Favourite part was	
Memorable Quotes	
My critic thoughts	

Director		-----/5
Cast		-----/5
Screenplay		-----/5
Cinematography		-----/5
Special effects/animation		-----/5
Music		-----/5
Customs		-----/5
Overall Score		-----/5

Will I watch it again?

I would recommend it to

Notes & Memories e.g. the tickets

MOVIES

Title	Date	time
Rating (G,PG, G13, R)	Genre/Style	

Storyline or plot	
My Favourite part was	
Memorable Quotes	
My critic thoughts	

Director		-----/5
Cast		-----/5
Screenplay		-----/5
Cinematography		-----/5
Special effects/animation		-----/5
Music		-----/5
Customs		-----/5
Overall Score		-----/5

Will I watch it again?

I would recommend it to

Notes & Memories e.g. the tickets

MOVIES

Title	| Date	|time
Rating (G,PG, G13, R)	|Genre/Style	

Storyline or plot	
My Favourite part was	
Memorable Quotes	
My critic thoughts	

Director		-----/5
Cast		-----/5
Screenplay		-----/5
Cinematography		-----/5
Special effects/animation		-----/5
Music		-----/5
Customs		-----/5
Overall Score		-----/5

Will I watch it again?

I would recommend it to

Notes & Memories e.g. the tickets

Title	Date	time
Rating (G,PG, G13, R)	Genre/Style	

Storyline or plot	
My Favourite part was	
Memorable Quotes	
My critic thoughts	

Director		-----/5
Cast		-----/5
Screenplay		-----/5
Cinematography		-----/5
Special effects/animation		-----/5
Music		-----/5
Customs		-----/5
Overall Score		-----/5

Will I watch it again?

I would recommend it to

Notes & Memories e.g. the tickets

MOVIES

Title	| Date	|time
Rating (G,PG, G13, R)	|Genre/Style	

Storyline or plot	
My Favourite part was	
Memorable Quotes	
My critic thoughts	

Director		-----/5
Cast		-----/5
Screenplay		-----/5
Cinematography		-----/5
Special effects/animation		-----/5
Music		-----/5
Customs		-----/5
Overall Score		-----/5

Will I watch it again?

I would recommend it to

Notes & Memories e.g. the tickets

Title	Date	time
Rating (G,PG, G13, R)	Genre/Style	

Storyline or plot	
My Favourite part was	
Memorable Quotes	
My critic thoughts	

Director -----/5

Cast -----/5

Screenplay -----/5

Cinematography -----/5

Special effects/animation -----/5

Music -----/5

Customs -----/5

Overall Score -----/5

Will I watch it again?

I would recommend it to

Notes & Memories e.g. the tickets

MOVIES

Title	| Date	|time
Rating (G,PG, G13, R)	|Genre/Style	

Storyline or plot	
My Favourite part was	
Memorable Quotes	
My critic thoughts	

Director	-----/5
Cast	-----/5
Screenplay	-----/5
Cinematography	-----/5
Special effects/animation	-----/5
Music	-----/5
Customs	-----/5
Overall Score	-----/5

Will I watch it again?

I would recommend it to

Notes & Memories e.g. the tickets

MOVIES

Title	Date	time
Rating (G,PG, G13, R)	Genre/Style	

Storyline or plot	
My Favourite part was	
Memorable Quotes	
My critic thoughts	

Director	-----/5
Cast	-----/5
Screenplay	-----/5
Cinematography	-----/5
Special effects/animation	-----/5
Music	-----/5
Customs	-----/5
Overall Score	-----/5

Will I watch it again?

I would recommend it to

Notes & Memories e.g. the tickets

MOVIES

Title	Date	time
Rating (G,PG, G13, R)	Genre/Style	

Storyline or plot	
My Favourite part was	
Memorable Quotes	
My critic thoughts	

Director		-----/5
Cast		-----/5
Screenplay		-----/5
Cinematography		-----/5
Special effects/animation		-----/5
Music		-----/5
Customs		-----/5
Overall Score		-----/5

Will I watch it again?

I would recommend it to

Notes & Memories e.g. the tickets

MOVIES

Title	Date	time
Rating (G,PG, G13, R)	Genre/Style	

Storyline or plot	
My Favourite part was	
Memorable Quotes	
My critic thoughts	

Director		-----/5
Cast		-----/5
Screenplay		-----/5
Cinematography		-----/5
Special effects/animation		-----/5
Music		-----/5
Customs		-----/5
Overall Score		-----/5

Will I watch it again?

I would recommend it to

Notes & Memories e.g. the tickets

MOVIES

Title	| Date	|time
Rating (G,PG, G13, R)	|Genre/Style	

Storyline or plot	
My Favourite part was	
Memorable Quotes	
My critic thoughts	

Director		-----/5
Cast		-----/5
Screenplay		-----/5
Cinematography		-----/5
Special effects/animation		-----/5
Music		-----/5
Customs		-----/5
Overall Score		-----/5

Will I watch it again?

I would recommend it to

Notes & Memories e.g. the tickets

MOVIES

Title	Date	time
Rating (G,PG, G13, R)	Genre/Style	

Storyline or plot	
My Favourite part was	
Memorable Quotes	
My critic thoughts	

Director		-----/5
Cast		-----/5
Screenplay		-----/5
Cinematography		-----/5
Special effects/animation		-----/5
Music		-----/5
Customs		-----/5
Overall Score		-----/5

Will I watch it again?

I would recommend it to

Notes & Memories e.g. the tickets

MOVIES

Title	| Date	|time
Rating (G,PG, G13, R)	|Genre/Style	

Storyline or plot	
My Favourite part was	
Memorable Quotes	
My critic thoughts	

Director	-----/5
Cast	-----/5
Screenplay	-----/5
Cinematography	-----/5
Special effects/animation	-----/5
Music	-----/5
Customs	-----/5
Overall Score	-----/5

Will I watch it again?

I would recommend it to

Notes & Memories e.g. the tickets

MOVIES

Title		Date	time
Rating (G,PG, G13, R)	Genre/Style	

Storyline or plot	
My Favourite part was	
Memorable Quotes	
My critic thoughts	

Director	-----/5
Cast	-----/5
Screenplay	-----/5
Cinematography	-----/5
Special effects/animation	-----/5
Music	-----/5
Customs	-----/5
Overall Score	-----/5

Will I watch it again?

I would recommend it to

Notes & Memories e.g. the tickets

Title	| Date	|time
Rating (G,PG, G13, R)	|Genre/Style	

Storyline or plot	
My Favourite part was	
Memorable Quotes	
My critic thoughts	

Director		-----/5
Cast		-----/5
Screenplay		-----/5
Cinematography		-----/5
Special effects/animation		-----/5
Music		-----/5
Customs		-----/5
Overall Score		-----/5

Will I watch it again?

I would recommend it to

Notes & Memories e.g. the tickets

MOVIES

Title	| Date	|time
Rating (G,PG, G13, R)	|Genre/Style	

Storyline or plot	
My Favourite part was	
Memorable Quotes	
My critic thoughts	

Director		-----/5
Cast		-----/5
Screenplay		-----/5
Cinematography		-----/5
Special effects/animation		-----/5
Music		-----/5
Customs		-----/5
Overall Score		-----/5

Will I watch it again?

I would recommend it to

Notes & Memories e.g. the tickets

MOVIES

Title	| Date	|time
Rating (G,PG, G13, R)	|Genre/Style	

Storyline or plot	
My Favourite part was	
Memorable Quotes	
My critic thoughts	

Director		-----/5
Cast		-----/5
Screenplay		-----/5
Cinematography		-----/5
Special effects/animation		-----/5
Music		-----/5
Customs		-----/5
Overall Score		-----/5

Will I watch it again?

I would recommend it to

Notes & Memories e.g. the tickets

Title	Date	time
Rating (G,PG, G13, R)	Genre/Style	

Storyline or plot	
My Favourite part was	
Memorable Quotes	
My critic thoughts	

Director		-----/5
Cast		-----/5
Screenplay		-----/5
Cinematography		-----/5
Special effects/animation		-----/5
Music		-----/5
Customs		-----/5
Overall Score		-----/5

Will I watch it again?

I would recommend it to

Notes & Memories e.g. the tickets

MOVIES

Title	Date	time
Rating (G,PG, G13, R)	Genre/Style	

Storyline or plot

My Favourite part was

Memorable Quotes

My critic thoughts

Director		-----/5
Cast		-----/5
Screenplay		-----/5
Cinematography		-----/5
Special effects/animation		-----/5
Music		-----/5
Customs		-----/5
Overall Score		-----/5

Will I watch it again?

I would recommend it to

Notes & Memories e.g. the tickets

MOVIES

Title	Date	time
Rating (G,PG, G13, R)	Genre/Style	

Storyline or plot	
My Favourite part was	
Memorable Quotes	
My critic thoughts	

Director		-----/5
Cast		-----/5
Screenplay		-----/5
Cinematography		-----/5
Special effects/animation		-----/5
Music		-----/5
Customs		-----/5
Overall Score		-----/5

Will I watch it again?

I would recommend it to

Notes & Memories e.g. the tickets

MOVIES

Title	Date	time
Rating (G,PG, G13, R)	Genre/Style	

Storyline or plot	
My Favourite part was	
Memorable Quotes	
My critic thoughts	

Director		-----/5
Cast		-----/5
Screenplay		-----/5
Cinematography		-----/5
Special effects/animation		-----/5
Music		-----/5
Customs		-----/5
Overall Score		-----/5

Will I watch it again?

I would recommend it to

Notes & Memories e.g. the tickets

MOVIES

Title	Date	time
Rating (G,PG, G13, R)	Genre/Style	

Storyline or plot

My Favourite part was

Memorable Quotes

My critic thoughts

Director	-----/5
Cast	-----/5
Screenplay	-----/5
Cinematography	-----/5
Special effects/animation	-----/5
Music	-----/5
Customs	-----/5
Overall Score	-----/5

Will I watch it again?

I would recommend it to

Notes & Memories e.g. the tickets

MOVIES

Title	Date	time
Rating (G,PG, G13, R)	Genre/Style	

Storyline or plot	
My Favourite part was	
Memorable Quotes	
My critic thoughts	

Director		-----/5
Cast		-----/5
Screenplay		-----/5
Cinematography		-----/5
Special effects/animation		-----/5
Music		-----/5
Customs		-----/5
Overall Score		-----/5

Will I watch it again?

I would recommend it to

Notes & Memories e.g. the tickets

MOVIES

Title	| Date	|time
Rating (G,PG, G13, R)	|Genre/Style	

Storyline or plot	
My Favourite part was	
Memorable Quotes	
My critic thoughts	

Director		-----/5
Cast		-----/5
Screenplay		-----/5
Cinematography		-----/5
Special effects/animation		-----/5
Music		-----/5
Customs		-----/5
Overall Score		-----/5

Will I watch it again?

I would recommend it to

Notes & Memories e.g. the tickets

MOVIES

Title	Date	time
Rating (G,PG, G13, R)	Genre/Style	

Storyline or plot	
My Favourite part was	
Memorable Quotes	
My critic thoughts	

Director		-----/5
Cast		-----/5
Screenplay		-----/5
Cinematography		-----/5
Special effects/animation		-----/5
Music		-----/5
Customs		-----/5
Overall Score		-----/5

Will I watch it again?

I would recommend it to

Notes & Memories e.g. the tickets

MOVIES

Title	Date	time
Rating (G,PG, G13, R)	Genre/Style	

Storyline or plot	
My Favourite part was	
Memorable Quotes	
My critic thoughts	

Director		-----/5
Cast		-----/5
Screenplay		-----/5
Cinematography		-----/5
Special effects/animation		-----/5
Music		-----/5
Customs		-----/5
Overall Score		-----/5

Will I watch it again?

I would recommend it to

Notes & Memories e.g. the tickets

MOVIES

Title	Date	time
Rating (G,PG, G13, R)	Genre/Style	

Storyline or plot	
My Favourite part was	
Memorable Quotes	
My critic thoughts	

Director	-----/5
Cast	-----/5
Screenplay	-----/5
Cinematography	-----/5
Special effects/animation	-----/5
Music	-----/5
Customs	-----/5
Overall Score	-----/5

Will I watch it again?

I would recommend it to

Notes & Memories e.g. the tickets

MOVIES

Title	Date	time
Rating (G,PG, G13, R)	Genre/Style	

Storyline or plot	
My Favourite part was	
Memorable Quotes	
My critic thoughts	

Director		-----/5
Cast		-----/5
Screenplay		-----/5
Cinematography		-----/5
Special effects/animation		-----/5
Music		-----/5
Customs		-----/5
Overall Score		-----/5

Will I watch it again?

I would recommend it to

Notes & Memories e.g. the tickets

MOVIES

Title	Date	time
Rating (G,PG, G13, R)	Genre/Style	

Storyline or plot	
My Favourite part was	
Memorable Quotes	
My critic thoughts	

Director		-----/5
Cast		-----/5
Screenplay		-----/5
Cinematography		-----/5
Special effects/animation		-----/5
Music		-----/5
Customs		-----/5
Overall Score		-----/5

Will I watch it again?

I would recommend it to

Notes & Memories e.g. the tickets

MOVIES

Title		Date	|time
Rating (G,PG, G13, R)	|Genre/Style	

Storyline or plot	
My Favourite part was	
Memorable Quotes	
My critic thoughts	

Director	-----/5
Cast	-----/5
Screenplay	-----/5
Cinematography	-----/5
Special effects/animation	-----/5
Music	-----/5
Customs	-----/5
Overall Score	-----/5

Will I watch it again?

I would recommend it to

Notes & Memories e.g. the tickets

MOVIES

Title	| Date	|time
Rating (G,PG, G13, R)	|Genre/Style	

Storyline or plot	
My Favourite part was	
Memorable Quotes	
My critic thoughts	

Director		-----/5
Cast		-----/5
Screenplay		-----/5
Cinematography		-----/5
Special effects/animation		-----/5
Music		-----/5
Customs		-----/5
Overall Score		-----/5

Will I watch it again?

I would recommend it to

Notes & Memories e.g. the tickets

Title	Date	time
Rating (G,PG, G13, R)	Genre/Style	

Storyline or plot	
My Favourite part was	
Memorable Quotes	
My critic thoughts	

Director	-----/5
Cast	-----/5
Screenplay	-----/5
Cinematography	-----/5
Special effects/animation	-----/5
Music	-----/5
Customs	-----/5
Overall Score	-----/5

Will I watch it again?

I would recommend it to

Notes & Memories e.g. the tickets

MOVIES

Title	| Date	|time
Rating (G,PG, G13, R)	|Genre/Style	

Storyline or plot	
My Favourite part was	
Memorable Quotes	
My critic thoughts	

Director	-----/5
Cast	-----/5
Screenplay	-----/5
Cinematography	-----/5
Special effects/animation	-----/5
Music	-----/5
Customs	-----/5
Overall Score	-----/5

Will I watch it again?

I would recommend it to

Notes & Memories e.g. the tickets

MOVIES

Title	Date	time
Rating (G,PG, G13, R)	Genre/Style	

Storyline or plot	
My Favourite part was	
Memorable Quotes	
My critic thoughts	

Director		-----/5
Cast		-----/5
Screenplay		-----/5
Cinematography		-----/5
Special effects/animation		-----/5
Music		-----/5
Customs		-----/5
Overall Score		-----/5

Will I watch it again?

I would recommend it to

Notes & Memories e.g. the tickets

MOVIES

Title	| Date	|time
Rating (G,PG, G13, R)	|Genre/Style	

Storyline or plot	
My Favourite part was	
Memorable Quotes	
My critic thoughts	

Director		-----/5
Cast		-----/5
Screenplay		-----/5
Cinematography		-----/5
Special effects/animation		-----/5
Music		-----/5
Customs		-----/5
Overall Score		-----/5

Will I watch it again?

I would recommend it to

Notes & Memories e.g. the tickets

Title	| Date	|time
Rating (G,PG, G13, R)	|Genre/Style	

Storyline or plot	
My Favourite part was	
Memorable Quotes	
My critic thoughts	

Director		-----/5
Cast		-----/5
Screenplay		-----/5
Cinematography		-----/5
Special effects/animation		-----/5
Music		-----/5
Customs		-----/5
Overall Score		-----/5

Will I watch it again?

I would recommend it to

Notes & Memories e.g. the tickets

MOVIES

Title	| Date	|time
Rating (G,PG, G13, R)	|Genre/Style	

Storyline or plot	
My Favourite part was	
Memorable Quotes	
My critic thoughts	

Director		-----/5
Cast		-----/5
Screenplay		-----/5
Cinematography		-----/5
Special effects/animation		-----/5
Music		-----/5
Customs		-----/5
Overall Score		-----/5

Will I watch it again?

I would recommend it to

Notes & Memories e.g. the tickets

Title	Date	time
Rating (G,PG, G13, R)	Genre/Style	

Storyline or plot

My Favourite part was

Memorable Quotes

My critic thoughts

Director	-----/5
Cast	-----/5
Screenplay	-----/5
Cinematography	-----/5
Special effects/animation	-----/5
Music	-----/5
Customs	-----/5
Overall Score	-----/5

Will I watch it again?

I would recommend it to

Notes & Memories e.g. the tickets

MOVIES

Title	Date	time
Rating (G,PG, G13, R)	Genre/Style	

Storyline or plot	
My Favourite part was	
Memorable Quotes	
My critic thoughts	

Director		-----/5
Cast		-----/5
Screenplay		-----/5
Cinematography		-----/5
Special effects/animation		-----/5
Music		-----/5
Customs		-----/5
Overall Score		-----/5

Will I watch it again?

I would recommend it to

Notes & Memories e.g. the tickets

MOVIES

Title	Date	time
Rating (G,PG, G13, R)	Genre/Style	

Storyline or plot	
My Favourite part was	
Memorable Quotes	
My critic thoughts	

Director		-----/5
Cast		-----/5
Screenplay		-----/5
Cinematography		-----/5
Special effects/animation		-----/5
Music		-----/5
Customs		-----/5
Overall Score		-----/5

Will I watch it again?

I would recommend it to

Notes & Memories e.g. the tickets

MOVIES

Title	| Date	|time
Rating (G,PG, G13, R)	|Genre/Style	

Storyline or plot	
My Favourite part was	
Memorable Quotes	
My critic thoughts	

Director	-----/5
Cast	-----/5
Screenplay	-----/5
Cinematography	-----/5
Special effects/animation	-----/5
Music	-----/5
Customs	-----/5
Overall Score	-----/5

Will I watch it again?

I would recommend it to

Notes & Memories e.g. the tickets

MOVIES

Title	| Date	|time
Rating (G,PG, G13, R)	|Genre/Style	

Storyline or plot	
My Favourite part was	
Memorable Quotes	
My critic thoughts	

Director		-----/5
Cast		-----/5
Screenplay		-----/5
Cinematography		-----/5
Special effects/animation		-----/5
Music		-----/5
Customs		-----/5
Overall Score		-----/5

Will I watch it again?

I would recommend it to

Notes & Memories e.g. the tickets

MOVIES

Title		Date	|time
Rating (G,PG, G13, R)	|Genre/Style	

Storyline or plot	
My Favourite part was	
Memorable Quotes	
My critic thoughts	